Bring Back That Loving Feeling

Light His Fire

© L.H.F. ENTERPRISES

Life is motion. Not to move forward is to move backward...
If your relationship is not getting better, it is getting worse.

Light His Fire Workbook

Table of Contents

SELF-IMPROVEMENT

"What have you got on improving other people?"

Session 1: Unconditional Love

How to get the most from Light His Fire™

♥   Be open minded
♥   Be willing to try
♥   Be patient
♥   Be honest with yourself
♥   Be introspective
♥   Be a good listener
♥   Be an active participant
♥   Be determined to improve

*"No job, no hobby, no activity on earth can compare with the
drama and the exhilarating experience of living with a man,
loving him, doing your best to understand his infinitely
complex mechanism and helping to make it hum and sing
and soar the way it was designed to do."*

—*Ruth Stafford Peale*—

A tunnel without cheese

If you put a rat in front of a bunch of tunnels and put cheese in one of them, the rat will go up and down the tunnels looking for the cheese. If every time you do the experiment you put the cheese down the fourth tunnel, eventually you'll get a successful rat. This rat knows the right tunnel and goes directly to it every time.

If you move the cheese out of the fourth tunnel and put it at the end of another tunnel, the rat still goes down the fourth tunnel. And, of course, gets no cheese. He then comes out of the tunnel, looks the tunnel over, and goes right back down the cheeseless fourth tunnel. Unrewarded, he comes out of the tunnel, looks the tunnels over again, goes back down the fourth tunnel again, and again finds no cheese.

Now the difference between a rat and a human being is that eventually the rat will stop going down the fourth tunnel and will look down the other tunnels, and a human being will go down the tunnel with no cheese forever. Rats, you see, are only interested in cheese. But human beings care more about going down the right tunnel.

It is belief which allows human beings to go down the fourth tunnel ad nauseam. They go on doing what they do without any real satisfaction, without any nurturing, because they come to believe that what they are doing is RIGHT. And they will do this forever, even if there is no cheese in the tunnel, as long as they believe in it and can prove that they are in the right tunnel.

Rating your relationship

INSTRUCTIONS:
Check the description that most applies to you. If some parts of the descriptions do not apply, cross them out. Feel free to add whatever you feel is necessary. Keep in mind that there can be no progress without your honest evaluation. Please answer honestly.

☒ OUTSTANDING: My relationship is nearly perfect. My mate would do anything for me. He tells me how much he loves me all the time.

☐ VERY GOOD: My mate loves me, but we do have a few minor problems. He is thoughtful. He often tells me how much he loves me.

☐ GOOD: Overall, I feel our relationship will endure. Although my mate does not tell me he loves me very often, I am confident that he does.

☐ TOLERABLE: Although we have no serious problems, our relationship is basically uninteresting. My mate takes me for granted most of the time. He seems to show very little interest in improving our relationship.

☐ UNHAPPY: I am disappointed with my relationship. My mate is short with me most of the time. He spends too much time away from home. He seldom tells me he loves me.

☐ MISERABLE: My mate is cold and indifferent to me. He acts like he has little or no respect for me. He is critical of most everything I do.

Two ways to look at everything

During the next six sessions, you will need to take responsibility for your own happiness. When focusing on yourself, you build better relationships with others.

It is not our responsibility to improve other people's behavior. Rather, it is our responsibility to improve ourselves. Since there are at least two ways to look at everything, we can take any given situation and try to examine it from different angles.

EXAMPLE:
During the next six weeks, you can complain about people -or you can take responsibility for yourself and realize that you feel upset because you find it hard to share some of the things you'd like to.

Two ways to look at everything

Look at this picture and write down what you see at first glance.

Two faces looking at each other

_____

_____

_____

Stare at the picture enclosed in the square. Do you see a man's face or do you see a woman with her hand to her face?

Two ways to look at everything

Two ways to look at everything

Everyone has a good side and a bad side. By learning how to use the word *and* in place of the word *but*, we would create fewer problems for ourselves and greatly enhance our relationships.

EXAMPLE:

1. My mate is a good provider *and* he likes to jog nearly every day. (This statement creates no problem.)

2. My mate is a good provider *but* he likes to jog and spends too much time doing it. (This statement creates a problem.)

INSTRUCTIONS:
Give an example of someone you have a relationship with that has a good and a bad side. Please be as specific as you can.

_____

_____

_____

_____

_____

_____

_____

_____

_____

Ironically, we tend to easily accept the good along with the bad outside of our relationship(s). For example, look at how unlikely it would be for us to make this statement — "I just took a job, but I am required to stand on my feet all day." Obviously, we would not complain to our employer about this "bad side" of the job — we would merely accept it and keep the above opinion to ourselves.

It would be foolish to complain and withdraw love from our pets just because they sometimes make a mess. It would be even more foolish to withdraw from our important relationships just because of few upsets and messes, regardless of how significant they may appear at the time. Unfortunately, too many people do!

She who waits for her Knight, must remember she will have to clean up after his Horse

Conflict

Rather than viewing conflict or disagreements as evidence that you no longer are in love, they should be viewed as inevitable — and a learning experience.

Remember, if two people agree on everything, then one person is not necessary in the relationship.

CONFLICT LEADS TO GROWTH.

IT DOES NOT HAVE TO LEAD TO DIVORCE!

"The biggest problem with the American family is that they actually think there should be no problems."

—*Bruno Bettleheim*—

Describe a time in your life when there was a great deal of conflict.

_____
_____
_____
_____
_____
_____
_____
_____
_____
_____

What lesson did you learn or what type of growth occurred as a result of that conflict?

_____
_____
_____
_____
_____
_____
_____
_____
_____

There may be a good side to his faults

How can you love someone *unconditionally* when there are so many things about him that you don't like? The answer:

♥ Adjust your attitude

♥ Fine-tune your thinking

In other words, to be human is to have faults as well as virtues!

Trash or treasure?

What you define as a fault is subjective — one woman's trash is another woman's treasure. For example:

♥ You feel your mate is too ambitious — some women feel their mates are too complacent and wish they were more aggressive.

♥ You feel your mate spends too much time with the children — some women feel their mates are self-centered and don't spend enough time with the family.

♥ You feel your mate is a too affectionate and wants to make love too often — some women complain that their mates aren't interested enough in sex.

In short, for every trait that you consider negative, there is another woman who would look at it a positive way.

Two ways of looking at everyone

Remember, there are at least two ways of looking at everyone. You can choose to look at your mate's personality in a negative way or decide you are going to concentrate on the positive aspects of his personality. Study and consider the following traits:

♥ Unenthusiastic

♥ Indecisive

♥ Egotistical

♥ Disorganized

♥ Naive

Now let's look at these traits more positively.

Unenthusiastic

Here is a man who is calm and soothing to be with. He usually is level-headed and well grounded. He doesn't get upset at trivial matters and isn't prone to mood swings. He's patient, consistent and low-key.

Indecisive

Here is a man who is open to all possibilities and usually sees many alternatives in any given situation. He's flexible, open-minded and philosophical.

Egotistical

Here is often a man with a brilliant mind who is goal-oriented. He focuses his energy on working hard at the office so he can provide financial security for his family. He is highly motivated and often forgets small details because he's concerned with the bigger picture. He's independent, confident and strong-willed.

Disorganized

Here is a man who is fun to be with. He has the ability to live in the present. He's not in a hurry and will make you stop and smell the roses. He's spontaneous, unpredictable and multi-faceted.

Naive

Here is a man who is good-natured. He's usually sensitive and puts people at ease. He's innocent, cheerful and sincere.

Don't make your love conditional

The first principle in making a love relationship work is to love someone *for who he is* — not what you fantasize he should be. Avoid making statements which can be interpreted as criticism.

EXAMPLE:

♥ "I'll love you *if* you earn more money!"

♥ "I'll love you *if* you will be more outgoing!"

♥ "I'll love you *if* you will stop watching sports on T.V. so much!"

♥ "I'll love you *if* you will just be a better father!"

♥ "I'll love you *if* you'll stop working late so much!"

The problem with conditional love

The problem with conditional love is that it is too impersonal. It requires a person to wonder whether he is:

♥ Worthy of your love

♥ Deserving of your love

♥ Meeting the requirements for your love

♥ Eligible for your love

UNQUALIFIED LOVE FOSTERS

THE IDEAL RELATIONSHIP.

Unqualified love is a gift given with *no strings attached*. Unqualified love means that there are:

♥   No prerequisites for your love

♥   No contingencies for your love

♥   No requirements for your love

The point is, we have to accept a man (and everyone else close to us) at face value — *the way he is* — part fault, part virtue.

> *"Unconditional love corresponds to one of the deepest longings, not only of the child, but of every human being; on the other hand, to be loved because of one's merit, because one deserves it, always leaves doubt; maybe I did not please the person whom I want to love me, maybe this, or that —there is always a fear that love could disappear. Furthermore, 'deserved' love easily leaves a bitter feeling that one is not loved for oneself, that one is loved only because one pleases, that one is, in the last analysis, not loved at all but used."*

> —Eric Fromm—
> <u>The Art of Loving</u>

> *"If you accept my love as a gift, it will enable you to grow. You need to know I love you whether you do your best or not so that you will have the strength to do your best."*

> —Powell—

INSTRUCTIONS:
Think of your mate as if he were divided into two distinct parts. Remember, there is no human being alive that doesn't have a good and a bad side.

What do I like least about my mate?

_____
_____
_____
_____
_____
_____
_____
_____
_____
_____

What do I like most about my mate?

_____
_____
_____
_____
_____
_____
_____
_____
_____
_____

From now on...concentrate on his good side

Which of the following are you most likely to do in order to change his behavior?

☐ Compare him with other men.

☐ Use yourself as the perfect role model.

☐ Read articles or passages from books, asking him why can't he be more of what they suggest.

☐ Tell him how unhappy he must feel, being like he is.

☐ Tell him that you deserve much more than what he's giving you.

☐ Suggest he go on a self-improvement project, take a special course, or anything else that can cause him to change.

Sometimes our behavior is worse than the fault we're annoyed about.

In order to get your way, do you respond by:

☐ Belittling

☐ Nagging

☐ Criticizing

☐ Ignoring

☐ Sarcasm

☐ Moaning and groaning

☐ Sighing, huffing, and puffing

☐ Embarrassing

☐ Gossiping to other women

☐ Withholding sex

You will always be tested

You need to be aware of one very important fact — your *unconditional* love is going to be tested often — for as long as your relationship exists.

Here are some examples of questions meant to test your love, followed by possible wrong and right responses you could make.

♥   *"What happens if I get this promotion and we have to move to another state?"*

WRONG RESPONSE — "What do you mean move? We aren't going anywhere! All of my friends live here!"

RIGHT RESPONSE — "I don't care where we live, as long as we're together!"

♥   *"What happens if I don't get that raise?"*

WRONG RESPONSE — "Don't be so pessimistic! If you continue to work hard, you'll get that raise!"

OR — "How are we supposed to keep the kids in college and keep up with inflation if you don't get that raise?"

RIGHT RESPONSE — "Nothing will happen!? We'll manage! All that matters is that we are together and that I love you!"

Describe a "What if" question that you have been asked in the past.

_____
_____
_____
_____
_____

What was your response?

_____
_____
_____
_____
_____

Give an example of a correct response.

_____
_____
_____
_____
_____

Why men fall in love

Men fall in love because of the way they feel about themselves when they are with you.

The majority of men, single or married, are captivated by a woman who makes them feel:

♥ Stronger

♥ More capable

♥ More intelligent

♥ More knowledgeable

♥ Sexier

Before Marriage

After Marriage

Can you remember how you felt when you first met that wonderful man? You could recite how great he was, and what marvelous attributes he possessed! With the passage of time, we tend to dwell on something entirely different.

When we first met this glorious man, we thought, "He is...":	*Now we have gotten into the habit of thinking, "He is...":*
Confident	Conceited
Soft spoken	Timid and weak
Mellow and calming	Passive and boring
Strong	Bully
Opinionated	Know-It-All
Affectionate	Oversexed
Humorous	Sarcastic
Ambitious	Money hungry
Athletic	Sports maniac
Sophisticated traveler	Compulsive nomad
Easygoing and relaxed	Apathetic and dull
Outgoing	Big mouth
Kind	Inconsiderate

If he met another woman, which side do you think she'd see?

Men and women enter into relationships differently

A man wants to feel like your hero forever. Once you start to concentrate on his faults and try to change him, the love you had in the beginning begins to die.

♥ WOMEN seem to go into a relationship saying:

"I know there are a lot of things about him that I don't like, but wait until I get through with him. You won't even recognize him."

♥ MEN, on the other hand, say:

"When I'm with this woman, I feel like a king. It's wonderful. I hope she never changes. I always want to feel like this."

Use this space to list some of your mate's traits, habits, physical characteristics, etc. that you have tried to change in the past.

_____

_____

_____

_____

_____

_____

_____

_____

_____

Opposites attract

Opposites attract — trite but true. Most people are attracted to someone who possesses traits that are lacking in themselves. For example:

♥ If you are spontaneous and love to do things on the spur of the moment — your mate is probably more cautious and thorough.

♥ If you love people and enjoy parties — your mate probably prefers quiet, intimate evenings alone with you.

♥ If you are a verbal woman who enjoys giving a detailed account and cannot say anything in a few words — your mate probably can recount an event in one sentence.

♥ If you are neat and organized — your mate is probably disorganized and leaves his clothes lying around everywhere.

♥ If you are a woman who puts the needs of others before her own — your mate is probably self-centered.

♥ If you are a woman that loves to spend money — your mate probably tries to hoard every penny.

♥ If you are an emotional woman — your mate is probably logical.

♥ If you are often tense and anxious — your mate is probably relaxed and easy going.

In short, your strengths are his weaknesses — and his strengths are your weaknesses. It is like two pieces of a puzzle that fit together.

♥ You must appreciate your mate for his characteristics

♥ You each have something to learn from the other

REMEMBER, we are all different. Not BETTER or WORSE, not good or bad, not right or wrong — JUST DIFFERENT. In fact, it is usually our differences that attract us to each other.

Look at the following chart. Put your first initial next to the characteristics that describe you and the first initial of your mate when it describes him. If they fit both of you, put both your initials next to the same word.

_____	Impulsive	_____	Careful
_____	Verbal	_____	Non-verbal
_____	Sociable	_____	Unsociable
_____	Friendly	_____	Unfriendly
_____	Approachable	_____	Unapproachable
_____	Emotional	_____	Logical
_____	Organized	_____	Disorganized
_____	Open-minded	_____	Opinionated
_____	Teacher	_____	Student
_____	Participant	_____	Observer
_____	Physical	_____	Intellectual
_____	Morning	_____	Evening
_____	Egotistical	_____	Self-sacrificing
_____	Relaxed	_____	Tense
_____	Negative	_____	Positive
_____	Spender	_____	Saver
_____	Romantic	_____	Practical
_____	Imaginative	_____	Realistic

Self-evaluation

Many women develop a superior attitude. In order to accept another person at face value, we must first look at ourselves objectively.

List 8 of your good qualities:

1. _____
2. _____
3. _____
4. _____
5. _____
6. _____
7. _____
8. _____

List 8 of your faults:

1. _____
2. _____
3. _____
4. _____
5. _____
6. _____
7. _____
8. _____

INSTRUCTIONS:
Use the space provided
to list your special
strengths.

INVENTORY OF PERSONAL STRENGTHS

Sports and Outdoor Activities:

Do you play any team sports, i.e. softball, bowling? Do you enjoy camping or hunting? Do you exercise regularly? What other sports or outdoor activities do you participate in?

_____

_____

_____

Hobbies and Crafts:

Do you teach or take classes related to crafts, such as weaving, potterymaking, or furniture refinishing? What other hobbies or interests do you pursue? Perhaps you are a history buff, family historian or amateur photographer.

_____

_____

_____

Expressive Arts:

Do people tell you you are artisitic? Do you enjoy dancing, writing, painting? Can you play a musical instrument? Are you in a choir? How do you express yourself creatively?

_____

_____

_____

Health:

Are you health concious? Do you keep up with the latest health news? Prepare healthy meals? Have regular medical checkups? Help other family members achieve better health?

_____

_____

_____

Education, Training and Related Areas:

Have you completed high school? College? Advanced study? Have you sought vocational or on-the-job training? Have you taken special courses or pursued self-education through study and organized reading? Have you achieved high grades or scholastic honors? Describe your educational achievements.

_____

_____

_____

Work, Vocation, Job or Position:

What is your work experience? What positions have you held? Have you been a manager or supervisor? Have you owned your own full-time or part-time business? Do you enjoy your work? What makes your work worthwhile (to you or others)? What is your work ethic?

_____

_____

_____

Special Aptitudes or Resources:

Are you intuitive? Do you trust your hunches? Do you have the ability to make things grow? Can you fix things or sell things? Are you good at math? What else are you good at?

_____

_____

_____

Strengths Through Family and Others:

Do you enjoy a loving, affectionate, supportive relationship with your mate? Are your relationships with your children or parents a source of satisfaction and strength? Do you have a strong network of supportive friends? How do your relationships strengthen you?

_____

_____

_____

Intellectual Strengths:

Are you the curious type? Do you enjoy problem solving? Are you open to new ideas? Are you a creative thinker? Do you enjoy learning new things? Describe ways in which you have demonstrated your intellectual strength.

_____

_____

_____

Aesthetic Strengths:

Are you awestruck by a beautiful sunset? Do you enjoy operas, concerts, art museums? Do you put effort into enhancing your physical surroundings? In what ways do you seek aesthetic fulfillment?

_____

_____

_____

Organizational Skills:

Are you a goal setter? Are you able to develop a plan of action and follow it through? Do people call on you to organize projects? Have you held leadership positions? Explain ways in which you have demonstrated organizational skills.

_____

_____

_____

Imaginative and Creative Strengths:

What creative solutions or new ideas have you devised in relation to home, family, work, or play? What are some of the ways you stretch your imagination and creativity?

_____

_____

_____

Relationship Strengths:

Some people have especially good people skills. Do you make friends in airports, restaurants, while shopping? Are you a good neighbor? Do you value people and treat them with respect, regardless of differences? Are you a good listener? What particular relationship skills do you possess?

_____
_____
_____

Spiritual Strengths:

Spirituality can be expressed in many ways. Are you a churchgoer or leader? Do you adhere to a set of religious or moral values in your daily activities? Do you find spiritual strength in nature? How do you nurture your spiritual side?

_____
_____
_____

Emotional Strengths:

Are you emotionally open? Can you express feelings such as happiness, anger, sadness? Can you give and receive affection? Are you spontaneous? Do you have empathy? Are you sensitive to the feelings of others? What role do your feelings and emotions play in your everyday life.

_____
_____
_____

Other Strengths:

How is your sense of humor? Can you laugh at yourself? How do you use humor to smooth out the rough spots?

_____
_____
_____

Do you have an adventurous spirit? How have you demonstrated that?

_____
_____
_____

Other Strengths:

Are you a risk taker? How have you risked, either with people, or in situations?

_____

_____

_____

Are you persistent? Relate ways you have stuck with a project or person, in spite of obstacles.

_____

_____

_____

Are you financially savvy? In what ways have you shown your financial ability?

_____

_____

_____

Are you culturally aware? Do you speak more than one language? Do you enjoy learning about other cultures?

_____

_____

_____

Have you spoken in public or made presentations?

_____

_____

_____

Are you well-groomed? Properly attired at all times? What is your sense of fashion?

_____

_____

_____

AFTER EVERY WEDDING COMES A MARRIAGE

— *Florence Littauer*

After 13 years of study-ing temperaments, Ms. Littauer designed the following charts:
(Taken from *After Every Wedding Comes a Marriage* by Florence Littauer. Copyright © 1984 by Harvest House Publishers, Eugene OR 97402)

SANGUINE

The Extrovert   *The Optimist*

The Talker

THE SANGUINE'S EMOTIONS:

Strengths	Weaknesses
Talkative, storyteller	Compulsive talker
Life-of-the-party	Exaggerates and elaborates
Good sense of humor	Dwells on trivia
Memory for color	Can't remember names
Holds on to listener	Scares others off
Emotional and demonstrative	Too happy for some
Enthusiastic	Has restless energy
Cheerful and bubbling over	Egotistical
Animated and expressive	Blusters and complains
Good on stage	Naive, gets taken in
Wide-eyed and innocent	Has loud voice and laugh
Lives in the present	Controlled by circumstances
Changeable disposition	Gets angry easily
Sincere at heart	Seems phony to some
Always a child	Never grows up

THE SANGUINE AT WORK:

Volunteers for jobs	Would rather talk
Thinks up new activities	Forgets obligations
Looks great on the surface	Doesn't follow through
Means well	Confidence fades fast
Has energy and enthusiasm	Undisciplined
Starts in a flashy way	Priorities out of order
Inspires others to join	Decides by feelings
Charms others to work	Easily distracted
	Wastes time talking
	Makes friends easily

	Strengths	Weaknesses
THE SANGUINE AS A FRIEND:	Loves people	Needs to be center stage
	Thrives on compliments	Wants to be popular
	Seems exciting	Looks for credit
	Envied by others	Dominates conversation
	Doesn't hold grudges	Interrupts and doesn't listen
	Apologizes quickly	Answers for others
	Prevents dull moments	Fickle and forgetful
	Likes spontaneous activities	Makes excuses
	Hates to be alone	Repeats stories
		Makes home fun
THE SANGUINE AS A PARENT:	Is liked by children's friends	Forgets children's appointments
	Turns disaster into humor	
	Is the circus master	Disorganized
	Keeps home in a frenzy	Doesn't listen to the whole story

MELANCHOLY

The Introvert   *The Pessimist*

The Thinker

	Strengths	Weaknesses
THE MELANCHOLY'S EMOTIONS:	Deep and thoughtful	Remembers the negatives
	Genius-prone	Moody and depressed
	Talented and creative	Enjoys being hurt
	Artistic or musical	Has false humility
	Philosophical and poetic	Off in another world
	Appreciative of beauty	Low self-image
	Sensitive to others	Has selective hearing
	Self-sacrificing	Self-centered
	Analytical	Too introspective
	Conscientious	Guilt feelings
	Serious or purposeful	Tends to hypochondria

	Strengths	**Weaknesses**
THE MELANCHOLY AT WORK:	Schedule-oriented Perfectionist Detail-conscious Persistent and thorough Orderly and organized Loves research Senses needs Sees the problems Finds creative solutions Needs to finish what he starts Likes charts, graphs, figures	Not people-oriented Depressed over imperfections Chooses difficult work Hesitant to start projects Spends too much time planning Prefers analysis to work Self-deprecating Hard to please Standards often too high Deep need for approval
THE MELANCHOLY AS A FRIEND:	Makes friends cautiously Content to stay in background Avoids causing attention Faithful and devoted Will listen to complaints Can solve others' problems Deep concern for other people Moved to tears with compassion Seeks ideal mate	Lives through others Insecure socially Withdrawn and remote Holds back affection Dislikes those in opposition Suspicious of people Antagonistic and vengeful Full of contradictions Skeptical of compliments
THE MELANCHOLY AS A PARENT:	Sets high standards Wants everything done right Keeps home in good order Picks up after children Sacrifices own will for others Encourages scholarship and talent	Puts goals beyond reach May discourage children May be too meticulous Sulks over disagreements Puts guilt upon children

CHOLERIC

The Extrovert   *The Optimist*

The Doer

	Strengths	Weaknesses

THE CHOLERIC'S EMOTIONS:	Born leader
	Dynamic and active
	Compulsive need for change
	Must correct wrongs
	Strong-willed and decisive
	Unemotional
	Not easily discouraged
	Independent and
	   self-sufficient
	Exudes confidence
	Can run anything
		Bossy
		Impatient
		Quick-tempered
		Can't relax
		Too impetuous
		Enjoys controversy and
		   argument
		Won't give up when losing
		Comes on too strong
		Inflexible
		Is not complimentary
		Dislikes tears and emotions
		Is unsympathetic

THE CHOLERIC AT WORK:	Goal-oriented Sees the whole picture Organizes well Seeks practical solutions Moves quickly to action Delegates work Insists on production Makes the goal Stimulates activity Thrives on opposition	Little tolerance for mistakes Doesn't analyze details Bored by trivia May make rash decisions May be rude or tactless Manipulates people Demanding of others End justifies the means Work may become his god Demands loyalty in the ranks
THE CHOLERIC AS A FRIEND:	Has little need for friends Will work for group activity Will lead and organize Is usually right Excels in emergencies	Tends to use people Dominates others Decides for others Knows everything Can do everything better Is too independent Possessive of friends and mate Can't say "I'm sorry" May be right, but unpopular

THE CHOLERIC AS A PARENT:

Strengths	*Weaknesses*
Exerts sound leadership	Tends to over-dominate
Establishes goals	Too busy for family
Motivates family to action	Gives answers too quickly
Knows the right answer	Impatient with poor performance
	Won't let children relax
	May send them into depression

PHLEGMATIC

The Introvert   *The Pessimist*

The Watcher

THE PHLEGMATIC'S EMOTIONS:

Strengths	*Weaknesses*
Low-key personality	Unenthusiastic
Easygoing and relaxed	Fearful and worried
Calm, cool, collected	Indecisive
Well-balanced	Avoids responsibility
Consistent life	Quiet will of iron
Quiet, but witty	Selfish
Sympathetic and kind	Too shy and reticent
Keeps emotions hidden	Too compromising
Happily reconciled to life	Self-righteous

THE PHLEGMATIC AT WORK:

Competent and steady	Not goal-oriented
Peaceful and agreeable	Lacks self-motivation
Has administrative ability	Hard to get moving
Mediates problems	Resents being pushed
Avoids conflicts	Lazy and careless
Good under pressure	Discourages others
Finds the easy way	Would rather watch

THE PHLEGMATIC AS A FRIEND:	Strengths	Weaknesses
	Easy to get along with	Dampens enthusiasm
	Pleasant and enjoyable	Stays uninvolved
	Good listener	Indifferent to plans
	Dry sense of humor	Judges others
	Enjoys watching people	Sarcastic and teasing
	Has many friends	Resists change
	Has compassion and concern	

THE PHLEGMATIC AS A PARENT:		
	Makes a good parent	Lax on discipline
	Takes time for the children	Doesn't organize home
	Is not in a hurry	Takes life too easy
	Can take the good with the bad	
	Doesn't get upset easily	

SUMMARY

1. Everyone has strengths as well as weaknesses. We have to learn to concentrate on a person's strengths.

2. Because someone is not a carbon copy of you does not mean he is wrong.

3. Everyone is unique. Each of us has different personality traits.

4. There is no such thing as one person being better than another. Different does not mean superior.

5. Opposites attract — we compliment each other. It is our differences which attract us to each other in the beginning.

6. Accept a man as he is, not what you want him to be. Acceptance is a peaceful state of mind when you finally realize that it is not our responsibility to make him over, but to appreciate him for who he is.

How to make a man feel accepted and appreciated

♥   First think about why you were attracted to him in the first place. What were the qualities you fell in love with?

♥   Don't have a superior attitude. Many women feel their way is the right way. Superiority destroys love. Do you want to be right or loved?

♥   Allow him to be human. He has strengths and weaknesses.

♥   Begin looking at his strengths. Life is to short to dwell on your mate's weaknesses. Concentrate on his good side.

♥   Verbalize your acceptance. Don't just think good thoughts — share them with your mate. He needs to hear the words.

HOMEWORK ASSIGNMENT — SESSION 1

Concentrate on your mate's good side.

1. Think of your relationship as brand new. Every time you are tempted to criticize, nag, demand or express disapproval of any kind, for one week, write it down. DON'T SAY IT. For the remainder of this course, concentrate on his good side only.   AND REMEMBER — love is blind. You do it with your plants and pets — do it with your mate.

2. When you tell a man you accept him the way he is, you set him free to be the best — without nagging or pushing. If you tell him, "I love you just the way you are," with no conditions attached, you strengthen his personal confidence — making him more responsible and more loving.

    ♥ Slip your arms around his waist one evening and say:
    "Honey, I've got to be the luckiest woman alive. I'm so glad you are part of my life. I can't imagine what my life would be like if I hadn't (met or married) you."

    ♥ Put your arms around him and tell him:
    "I really do love you for who you are. I know sometimes we have different views and a different way of doing things, but that's why I fell in love with you. You are so exciting to live with, and I get so much out of being with you. I wouldn't trade you for any other man in the whole world."

He may test you.

Remember, he may test you with a statement such as "Oh, yeah! What about Tom Selleck?"

Your reply should be:

"Are you kidding?   He doesn't hold a candle to you. You don't have any competition!"

"Blessed are the married ones who strive first of all to make their mates happy rather than good!"

— Glen Clark —

Session 2: Admiration and Appreciation

Request to a wife

"Dear wife, I need adoring looks,
The kind I read about in books
I want esteem, I want affection
Please, darling, beam in my direction.

"Don't, dearest, frown and squint your eyes.
Don't cut me down to proper size
Oh, do not fear and do not doubt me.
I want to hear the good about me.

"So, if you'd be in married clover,
Make over me,
Don't make me over."

— *Richard Armour* —

"Dear Ann Landers,

"Why would any husband adore a lazy, messy, disorganized, addlebrained wife? The woman next door brags that the minute her kids could reach the sink and the stove she taught them to fix their own breakfast so she could sleep. Her house looks like they moved in yesterday. For two years she has been saying, `We're not settled yet.'

"She never cooks a meal. Everything is in cans, or frozen, or sent out for. Her kids eat so much Chinese food from the place around the corner I wouldn't be surprised if their eyes began to slant. Yet this slob's husband treats her like a Dresden doll. He calls her 'poopsie' and 'pet' and covers the telephone with a blanket when he goes to work so she can get her rest. On weekends he does the laundry and marketing.

"I get up at 6 a.m. every morning and fix my husband a farmer's breakfast. I make his shirts because he doesn't like the ones in the stores. I bake my own bread and rolls and I even put up my own tomato juice to please him. My house is spotless. You can eat off the floors.

"If my husband ever emptied a wastebasket for me I'd faint. Once I phoned him at work and asked him to drop by the store and pick up a loaf of bread. He swore at me for five minutes. I say the more you do for a man the less he appreciates you. What goes on, anyway?"

— The Moose (that's what he calls me.) —

"Dear Moose,

"No man ever loved a woman because she kept the house spotless or baked bread for him.

"The slob next door makes her husband feel important, loved and needed. She has learned how to keep her marriage at an even keel and it has paid off.

"You can call her addlebrained if you want to — and maybe she is — but when it comes to handling her husband she can teach some Phi Beta Kappas a few things."

— Ann Landers —

Don't wait for some future time to tell your mate how much you love, respect and admire him. DO IT TODAY!

Say it now!

"If with pleasure you are viewing
    Anything a man is doing.
If you prize him, if you love him,
    Tell him now.

"Don't withhold your approbation
    'Til the Parson makes oration,
And he lies with lilies on his brow.

"For no matter how you shout it
    He won't really know about it,
He won't count the teardrops
    That you shed.

"If you think some praise is due him
    Now's the time to pass it to him,
For he cannot read his tombstone
    When he's dead."

— Anonymous —

The sad truth is:

Most women are complimented on their physical appearance every day.

Unfortuantely, men rarely receive compliments on their masculine appearance.

IMPORTANT: To arouse your mate's love — and get YOUR needs fulfilled — you must make your mate feel good about HIS MANHOOD!

Take a moment, RIGHT NOW, and list the six "masculine physical qualities" you adore most in your mate.

1. _____
2. _____
3. _____
4. _____
5. _____
6. _____

The following are some physical masculine qualities worth noting:

♥ Take notice of his chest

♥ Take notice of his sexy eyes

♥ Take notice of his masculine, broad shoulders

♥ Take notice of his hands

♥ Take notice of his powerful legs

♥ Take notice of his voice

♥ Take notice of the way he walks

♥ Take notice of his sexual performance

♥ Take notice of his height

♥ Take notice of his strong arms

♥ Take notice of his handsome face

♥ Take notice of his incredible smile

♥ Take notice of his great buns

♥ Take notice of anything — *and I mean anything* — that makes him a man.

Examples:

Another wonderful way to accomplish this is to compare him to well-known masculine role models.

> Rambo
> Incredible Hulk
> Superman
> Tarzan
> Rocky
> Hercules
> Conan (The Barbarian)
> King Kong
> Adonis
> Cassanova

Why is this so important?

Masculinity is very important to a man. When you notice his physical attributes, you make him feel manly. You then become indispensable to his happiness.

Your mate, in turn will be:

♥   Kinder towards you

♥   More helpful to you

♥   More romantic with you

♥   More complimentary to you

♥   More thoughtful towards you

♥   More protective of you

It's his masculinity that counts.

Any man will appreciate his mate's praise — but it's his *manhood* that he longs to have recognized!

Without his masculinity, your mate will become unmotivated.

Mr. Jim Sanderson, whose column "The Liberated Male" appears regularly in the Los Angeles Times, wrote about this subject in an article titled "Viewing Men as Sex Objects."

—Reprinted with Permission

Viewing Men as Sex Objects

"Every woman resents the way males constantly focus on her body. Every woman would like to be admired for her mind and her talent too — for what she can do and not just what she is.

"It's just the reverse for a male. We're tired of praise for what we can do; we'd all just love to be sex objects once in a while. Women say they hate to be ogled by construction workers, but I tell you if the girls in the beauty parlor want to lean out the door and whistle as I walk by, well hell, ladies, what time would be convenient for you?

"Do men really need this? Sure we do. You don't think we spend all that time in front of the mirror just shaving, do you? All we're really waiting for is a woman to come up, put her arms around us and whisper: "You're adorable."

"Ah, come on, you say, gross flattery for grown men? You're right — flattery will never make it. But that rare loving compliment lingers long. Inside every tycoon there is an 18-year-old boy with a full head of hair and flat stomach, who still cherishes his high school graduation night because some terrific girl told him he had sexy eyes.

"As teen-agers, we males worried as much about our supposed physical deficiencies as girls did, and we haven't necessarily forgotten. Who was there, after all, to say that our fears were groundless? Our mothers?

"Meanwhile, let me tell you my own most memorable physical compliment:

"All men love to watch women undress — the slower the better. But I recall one occasion when a woman seemed to be observing my own disrobing with equal interest. When I stood revealed in all my pristine glory, she murmured: "Ah, at last I know what Michelangelo meant..."

"This Delphic pronouncement terrorized me for a moment. Since things seemed to have been progressing excellently well between us. I had to assume she had made me an enormous gift: she had said right out loud that she loved my body.

(Continued on next page)

"I was, of course, suitably grateful. But what had the famed sculptor actually said? I never dared ask her. I imagined it as something like: "The male figure projects a sublimity that reaches beyond female grace."

"On the other hand, what if he had stared at his male model and snorted: "Men really are an ugly bunch of brutes, but I suppose I'll have to do the best I can."

"Frankly, I've fretted about this ever since. If anybody happens to know the truth about Michelangelo, please tell me, will you? We males are terribly insecure."

— Jim Sanderson —

We all want to matter

All people, male and female, want to matter in a positive way. One of the most rewarding feelings people can have comes from impacting someone in a positive way.

Unfortunately, if we can't matter in a positive way, we often elect to matter in a negative way. After all, that's psychologically better than not mattering at all. That's often the reason people have:

♥ Marital problems

♥ Relationship problems

♥ Discipline problems

A Mother's Praise Makes a Difference

My 14-year-old son Mark is the stone wall I'm always batting my head against. To say he's stubborn as a mule is an insult... to the mule. Needless to say, trying to get Mark to do what I want him to is a difficult proposition at best.

I don't have the fear factor going for me like my 6-foot-tall husband. I'm much shorter, and the dimples don't help. So my method for getting cooperation from Mark has had to slowly evolve from a source based on common sense instead of muscle.

One of the first things I had to do was to set my anger at Mark aside and look for something good to say about him. What a toughie! I was so in the habit of finding fault that I practically choked on my first compliments. But, after a while, a funny, wonderful thing happened. Mark began responding. He drank up praise like a dried sponge thrown in a rain puddle. Slowly but steadily he began to deserve more and more of my praise. When these new, more positive behaviors repeated themselves, I made sure I took time to notice and reinforce my praise. Nothing big, just "Nice job, Mark." Or "Thanks for remembering to take out the trash."

Finally, and I feel, most importantly, I came to realize one simple truth: Most of the time I had been kinder, more understanding and much more polite to total strangers than I had to my own son. My behavior changed; therefore, Mark's behavior changed.

REMEMBER:

A man wants to:

♥   Feel special

♥   Matter more than anything — or anyone — in your life

♥   Be told he makes a difference — **constantly**

The German author Goethe said:

"If you treat a man as he is, he'll stay as he is, but if you treat him as if he ought to be and could be, he will become the bigger and better man."

Appreciate and admire your man

Along with making your mate feel like a "sex object" once in a while, it is important that you appreciate and admire your man:

♥ For what he does

♥ For what he says

♥ For what he stands for

How to find traits to appreciate and admire

The best way to focus on things you appreciate and admire in your mate is to:

♥ *Think* about what he is saying or doing

♥ *Observe* him carefully; pay attention to his mannerisms, his character and his strengths

♥ *Listen* to what he says. Pay attention to what he's really saying and feeling — not just his words

Expressing admiration

When you express admiration regarding your mate's masculinity, it is important be:

♥ Specific

♥ Sincere

Marriage Advice

Let your love be stronger than your hate or anger.
Learn the wisdom of compromise, for it is better to bend a little than to break.
Believe the best rather than the worst.
People have a way of living up — or down — to your opinion of them.
Remember that true friendship is the basis for any lasting relationship. The person you choose to marry is deserving of the courtesies and kindnesses you bestow on your friends.
Please hand this down to your children and your children's children. The more things change, the more they are the same. — Jane Wells (1886).

The following are examples of compliments you can give. Look at the list and see how many you can put into practice immediately.

Compliment him for the things he does:

♥ If he washes the car —
Tell him how much you appreciate the pride he takes in keeping the car clean.

♥ If he fixes the car —
Tell him how lucky you are to have someone with so much mechanical ability.

♥ If he fixes things around the house —
Sing, "It's so nice to have a man around the house."

♥ If he exercises —
Tell him how wonderful it is to have a man who is in great shape and takes pride in his body.

♥ If he's taking classes —
Tell him you love his quest for knowledge.

♥ If he's on any volunteer committees —
Tell him how wonderful he is to give his time to causes.

♥ If he plays with the children —
Tell him how lucky the children are to have a father like him.

♥ If he plays with the dog —
Tell him how terrific it is to have a strong man who also has a tender side.

♥ If he earns a great deal of money —
Tell him you never dreamed you'd have the life-style he has provided for you.

Compliment him for the things he says:

♥ If he's funny —
Tell him you love his sense of humor and how great it makes you feel.

♥ If he's complimentary —
Tell him how lucky you are to have a man who notices.

♥ If he's always dreaming —
Tell him you love him because he is goal-oriented and thinking of the future.

♥ If he solves a problem —
Tell him how much his logic improves the quality of your life.

♥ If he's very verbal —
Tell him he's the "life of the party," how much you love to listen to him, and how he always makes people feel at ease.

♥ If he's nonverbal —
Tell him what a good listener he is, and what a calming influence he has on you.

Compliment him for the things he stands for:

♥ If he's honest —
Tell him how much you love that quality.

♥ If he's loyal —
Tell him how wonderful it is to be able to trust him.

♥ If he's dependable —
Tell him how secure you feel being with someone you can always depend on.

♥ If he's a risk-taker —
Tell him you love his courage to stand behind what he believes in.

♥ If he's confident —
Tell him that his belief in himself makes you believe in him.

The 3 "A's"

Every man wants to be...

♥   Accepted
For who he is, not what you want him to be

♥   Appreciated
Appreciate means to raise in value. It is the opposite of depreciate, or lower in value

♥   Admired
Looked up to, respected

Do any of these EXCUSES describe why you don't stroke your mate?

Barriers to the 3 "A's"

1.   A feeling of awkwardness when expressing a compliment.

2.   A failure to accept your mate at "face value."

3.   A belief that your mate is already too self-centered.

4.   A feeling that your mate doesn't have any valuable qualities that you can observe at this time.

5.   He becomes very embarrassed when you pay him a compliment and asks you to stop.

IMPORTANT:

- It takes four positive statements to offset one negative one.

- If a negative statement is made in front of other people, it has double the impact.

Do you ever do any of the following without realizing the negative impact it has?

1. Tell everyone that the reason you're working is because your mate doesn't make enough money.

2. Let him know that he could never make it without you.

3. Tell people how much more you had when living with your parents.

4. When he's excited about a new idea, tell him how ridiculous it is.

5. If he complains about his job, tell him that he's lucky he has one and he couldn't do any better.

6. If he's excited about an accomplishment, act bored or be too busy to listen.

7. When he repeats a particular story to friends, roll your eyes and say "How many times do I have to listen to this?"

8. If he's trying to fix something himself, insist he call in a repairman instead.

9. Tell him he's losing his hair or physique.

10. Tell him he's too oversexed or undersexed.

11. Tell your friends how cheap he is and that he never wants to spend any money.

12. Let everyone know he's never around when you need him.

Be honest and answer the following questions. Give specific examples:

1. Most of the time, do I build him up or tear him down?
   _____
   _____
   _____

2. Do I usually encourage him or do I discourage him?
   _____
   _____
   _____

3. When he talks, do I give him my undivided attention or am I thinking about something else?
   _____
   _____
   _____

4. If he confides in me, do I violate that confidence by telling other people or do I protect and guard that confidence?
   _____
   _____
   _____

5. Do I emphasize his strengths and minimize his weaknesses, or do I point out his weaknesses and ignore his strengths?
   _____
   _____
   _____

6. Do I treat my mate like he's the most special person in the world or am I more giving to strangers?
   _____
   _____
   _____

We lie to other people all the time to make them feel better. For example:

The people you love deserve the most

♥   If a guest were to break one of your dishes and become upset and apologetic, your response would probably be:

"Don't worry about it, it's not that important."

On the other hand, what might you say to your mate? Does this sound familiar?

"Why can't you be more careful! I can't believe you did that."

♥   If an acquaintance came to you near tears, complaining that she has gained five pounds and looks fat in her bathing suit, you would probably say:

"Don't be silly. You're a knockout in a bikini!"

On the other hand, what might you say to your mate? Does this ring a bell?

"Of course you've put on weight! The way you eat, you're lucky it's only five pounds!"

Give the people you love what you usually reserve for strangers!

In other words, build up your mate — say something positive. Help your mate feel good about himself by giving him:

♥   Praise
♥   Compliments
♥   Appreciation
♥   Admiration
♥   Acceptance

The following ad appeared in the "Personal Section" of a New York newspaper:

"I am 32, 6 feet tall, handsome, well built, athletic, intelligent, absolutely amazing and completely perfect in every way. I'd like to meet a woman who'll humor me when I get like this."

HOMEWORK ASSIGNMENT — SESSION 2

Let him know you appreciate him

1. Once a day, give your mate a compliment. Compliment him on:

    ♥   What he does

    ♥   What he says

    ♥   What he stands for

2. One day this week tell him how much *he matters* to you and how happy and proud you are to be part of his life.

Ask your mate to join you in the following exercise:

3. Have your mate write down ten things he really likes about you and you do the same for him. (Remember to include at least one or two physical attributes.) After you're both done, read your lists to each other. Be sure you take time to discuss the lists. Don't just hand them to each other.

    _____

    _____

    _____

    _____

    _____

    _____

    This is also a wonderful exercise to do with your children. If they are quite young, you might want them to list just five things they like about you, and you do the same for them.

4. This week, compliment three people you don't know. Instead of telling them to have a nice day — *make their day!*

Session 3: Communication

In business, poor communication can lead to disaster and financial failure.

In international affairs, it can lead to war.

In personal relationships, poor communication can lead to partners becoming strangers and the eventual breakup of the relationship.

What is communication?

Communication is more than just verbalization and hearing the words someone speaks. Good communication takes place when someone:

♥ Hears what you are saying

♥ Understands what you mean

♥ Validates what you are feeling

In a study conducted to determine what makes up *the total message* in communication, it was found that:

♥ Words make up 7 percent of the total message

♥ Non-verbal communication, such as body language and facial expression, make up 55 percent of the total message

♥ Tone of voice, including sighs, make up 38 percent of the total message

EXAMPLES:

Here are some examples where the spoken words don't necessarily convey the real message.

♥ Your mate is reading the newspaper. You ask him if he would like to go out tonight to dinner and a movie. Without looking up he says, "Yeah, sure. Whatever."

What message did you get?

_____

_____

_____

♥ Your mate senses there is something bothering you. He asks you what's wrong. You mutter, "Nothing," as you slam the cabinet door.

What message did your body language send?

_____
_____
_____

♥ Your mate tells a story you've heard many times before. You remark, "That's the tenth time I've heard that story."

What message did your words convey?

_____
_____
_____

♥ You've just made love and you are silent.

What does your silence say?

_____
_____
_____

♥ As your mate is talking to you, you look at your watch.

What message do you send?

_____
_____
_____

Sometimes it's not what you say, but how you say it, or even what you don't say, that creates bad feelings.

In all of these cases, the non-verbal message was different from the verbal message.

People are paid to solve problems on the job. At work, we are often are expected to evaluate and critique certain situations. In personal relationships, however, it's just the opposite. When someone you love comes to you and relates a situation or a problem, they don't want you to:

♥   Give a solution

♥   Come up with an answer

♥   Be critical

In personal relationships, people want to be understood and to have their feelings validated.

What sorts of things worry or upset your mate ?

☐   His weaknesses or a particular inability

☐   Health problems

☐   Work-related problems

☐   Overwhelming responsibilities

☐   Difficulty coping with a particular situation

☐   Insufficient money or lack of security

☐   Uncertainty about the future

☐   Lack of acceptance by other people

☐   World events

☐   Other

_____

_____

_____

When your mate risks telling you his feelings, do you:

☐ Offer a solution to his problem?

☐ Tell him he shouldn't feel that way?

☐ Tell him not to worry?

☐ Tell him he's making a *mountain out of a molehill?*

☐ Tell him not to be so negative?

☐ Tell him all of the things he should be thankful for?

☐ Tell him to lighten up; that he has no control over what happens, and that whatever *will be, will be?*

☐ Ignore what he is saying, because you're too busy to listen to such trivia?

☐ Try to make him feel better by telling him about someone who's in a worse situation?

☐ Say, "If you think you've got problems, wait 'til I tell you mine"?

When you respond to your mate's self-revelation in any of these ways, you send at least one of the following messages:

♥ I am a better person than you are

♥ I am smarter than you are

♥ I want you to change

♥ I don't trust you to work this out by yourself

♥ Your feelings aren't important

♥ I think you are doing something bad (or wrong)

♥ I could handle this problem easily

Giving your mate such negative messages can affect future communication in any number of undesirable ways. For example, your mate may:

♥ Stop telling you what's wrong

♥ Stop telling you what happened

♥ Become very defensive

♥ Start an argument with you

♥ Attack you verbally

♥ Resent you

♥ Feel inferior or inadequate

♥ Feel guilty

♥ Feel hurt

Communication is an art

To keep the lines of communication open in your relationship, you must let your mate know that you care about his feelings and opinions.

Always let him know that:

- ♥ You understand his feelings

- ♥ His feelings are important

- ♥ You respect his ideas although they may be different than yours

- ♥ He is entitled to his point of view

- ♥ You are interested in what happens to him

- ♥ You want to comfort him

- ♥ You accept him for who he is

To communicate these positive messages:

Remember, feelings are not right or wrong— they just are.

- ♥ Put yourself in his shoes

- ♥ Validate his feelings

- ♥ Give him your undivided attention. (This includes eye contact.)

- ♥ Touch him. Give him a hug, a kiss, or a pat on the back.

Learning to listen

There is an ancient proverb which says:

"We are given one mouth and two ears. Therefore, we are supposed to listen twice as much as we talk. Otherwise we would have been given two mouths and one ear."

To be a better listener, remember these important rules:

♥ You can't listen and talk at the same time. Keep your mouth closed and your ears open.

♥ Listen with your mind, as well as your ears. If you're busy thinking about what you're going to say next, you aren't listening. Keep your mind focused on what he is saying.

♥ Listen with your heart. Watch for the non-verbal clues that tell you what your mate really means.

EXERCISE:

In each of these scenarios, circle the answer that you think is best.

1. The promotion your mate had been hoping for was given to a co-worker. What should you say?

   a. John's been there much longer than you have.
   b. I'm sure your boss had a good reason for giving him the promotion.
   c. You'll probably get the next promotion.
   d. You must feel terrible. I know how much you were counting on that promotion.

Using your own words, write in other appropriate responses in the space provided.

_____

_____

_____

_____

2.   A friend tells you that her mate has called off their upcoming marriage. He's found someone new. What should you say?

   a.   Don't worry about it. He's not worth getting upset over.
   b.   I'm so sorry. You must be very disappointed.
   c.   I never liked him anyway.
   d.   There's lots of fish in the sea. You'll see. I'm sure you'll meet a wonderful new man in no time.

   _____
   _____
   _____
   _____

3.   Your child reveals how scared he is about a test he has to take. What should you say?

   a.   If you study hard, you'll have nothing to worry about.
   b.   It's only one tenth of your grade. Don't make such a big deal about it.
   c.   Worrying doesn't help. Just have a positive attitude. If you're negative about it, you're sure to fail.
   d.   Sweetheart, it's natural to be concerned. I know you want to do well, but all you can do is give it your best effort.

   _____
   _____
   _____
   _____

4. Your friend's house has been burglarized. What should you say?

   a. Just be thankful you weren't home.
   b. At least they didn't take anything irreplaceable.
   c. You should hear what happened to the Smiths when their house was robbed.
   d. How awful! What a violation of your privacy. You must be very frightened. I'll bet you don't even want to go home.

   _____
   _____
   _____
   _____

5. Your husband is worried about money and his job security. What should you say?

   a. You've been working too many hours.
   b. You need to spend more time with me and the children.
   c. You'd better "shape up or ship out."
   d. It must be a heavy burden to be responsible for earning a living and supporting this family. You are a wonderful man to be so concerned about our welfare and I love you very much.

   _____
   _____
   _____
   _____

Your mate needs your shoulder—not your mouth!

When someone has experienced a hurt, loss, or disappointment, or is feeling anxiety or fear, be assured that there is nothing you can say to make them feel better. Your only goal should be to *really listen* and to validate their feelings. This is more comforting and helpful than saying "the right thing" and helps bring about a feeling of closeness.

If your mate were to tell you what he wants from you, he'd say:

> *"Please just listen to me. I want to share what happened to me today and how I feel about it. I don't want any advice or answers. I just want you to care about me and understand what I'm feeling."*

Sometimes your advice really is wanted.

Ninety-five percent of the time when someone confides in you, they don't want advice, but about five percent of the time, they do. When your mate wants your advice, you'll hear the request loud and clear:

♥ Honey, could you help me solve this problem.

♥ I really need your advice.

♥ Tell me what you would do if your were in my situation.

♥ I'm so confused. Help me sort out a solution.

When you are asked for advice:

♥ Ask questions, so that you get a clear picture of his point of view.

♥ Give your opinion, using words that indicate insight such as "I feel." Don't say "I think," or "I know."

♥ Give him several choices.

♥ Leave the final decision up to him.

Accepting gifts graciously

Most men hate to shop. When your mate makes the effort to buy you a gift, he is giving you far more than a sweater, a piece of jewelry, or a bottle of perfume. He is giving you a gift of love.

Concentrate on the person, not the present.

How many times have you returned or exchanged a gift given to you by your mate?

☐　0

☐　1 – 5

☐　6 – 10

☐　More than 10 times

How often have you said something like:

♥　It's much too expensive.

♥　I could have gotten it for less.

♥　I don't really need this.

♥　You've been taken.

Always express your appreciation for his thoughtfulness.

When you are critical of a gift given to you, what message are you communicating?

_____

_____

_____

_____

The gift of touch

Another way of communicating is through the gift of touch. A good salesperson knows that touch helps establish rapport and a feeling of connection. People who live alone, live longer and healthier lives if they have a pet to touch and care for. Babies in orphanages who are not picked up and held can literally die from lack of touch.

Other Interesting facts about touch:

1) We have become a dog- and cat-petting society. We give animals what human beings needs the most.

2) The times when we are the most unlovable are the times when we need to be touched the most.

3) Human beings have been known to die from lack of touch.

4) When we touch another person, we make a connection.

5) Hugging and being hugged causes the brain to release endorphins—chemicals which produce a natural "high."

6) Opposites attract. It's not an accident when someone who has trouble touching is attracted to a person who is very "touchy-feely."

7) Touching is a behavior that can be learned. If you weren't raised in a family that touched, you need to learn this important skill now!

HOMEWORK ASSIGNMENT — SESSION 3

1. Schedule a minimum of thirty minutes every day for you and your mate to communicate. Take turns sharing the events of your day. Have each partner concentrate on what the other is saying, acknowledging what they hear, and validating the other person's feelings.

2. Start a touch program. Don't let your relationship suffer from *skin hunger*.

3. If he has given you a gift recently, wear it, display it, or use it. Acknowledge how lucky you are to have such a thoughtful mate and—if you haven't been appreciative enough in the past—apologize now.

Session 4: Romance Is A Decision

The best gift you can ever give your children is a loving relationship with your mate.

> *"Your lips cover me with kisses;*
> *Your love is better than wine;*
> *There is a fragrance about you;*
> *The sound of your name recalls it.*
> *No woman could keep from loving you.*
> *Take me with you, and we'll run away;*
> *Be my king and take me to your room.*
> *We will be happy together, drink deep*
> *And lose ourselves in love."*
>
> —Song of Songs, 1:2-4—

When was the last time the two of you went out on a date:

♥ Without children?

♥ Without relatives?

♥ Without friends or neighbors?

☐ 0 – 6 months ☐ 6 – 12 months
☐ 1 – 2 years ☐ 2 years or more

How long has it been since the two of you went away for an overnight stay or a weekend at a hotel?

☐ 0 – 6 months ☐ 6 – 12 months
☐ 1 – 2 years ☐ 2 years or more

How long has it been since the two of you went on a trip or a vacation alone for an entire week?

☐ 0 – 6 months ☐ 6 – 12 months
☐ 1 – 2 years ☐ 2 years or more

Formula for a successful relationship

♥ Make one night a week *date night*

♥ Once every three months have a *weekend away* (or, at the very least, an overnight stay at a hotel with an early check in and a late check out)

♥ Once a year take a *one-week (7-day) vacation*— just the two of you—without children, relatives, or friends!

Cost of going versus cost of not going

Cost of Going	Cost of not Going
• Time	• Distancing from each other
• Money	• Buildup of stress
• Guilt	• Nothing to anticipate
• Worry	• Missing out on having a lover and an affair
	• Illness
	• Anger

What other costs can you think of for going? For not going?

_____

_____

_____

_____

_____

_____

Corporate model of a relationship

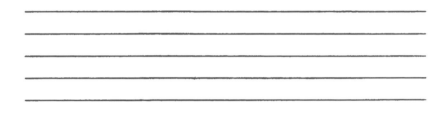

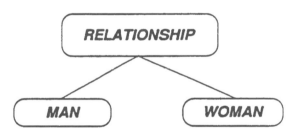

Relationship = Corporation
Husband and Wife = Officers of the Corporation

A relationship often requires you to do things you may not want to do or be in the mood to do.

♥ You may not want to take a walk with your mate, but your relationship requires it.

♥ You may not want to go away on a vacation together, but your relationship requires it.

♥ You may not want to spend thirty minutes of uninterrupted time with your mate, but your relationship requires it.

What have you done lately to make your relationship a top priority?

_____

_____

_____

_____

_____

_____

_____

_____

The greeting

The first three minutes of a greeting set the tone for the rest of the time you are together.

Think back to when you first fell in love. How did you greet your lover after being apart for the day?

- ♥ You smiled

- ♥ You embraced him

- ♥ You kissed him

- ♥ You inquired about his day

How do you think he felt?

_____

_____

_____

_____

_____

Compare that greeting to how you greet the most important person in your life now:

♥ Are you on the phone?

♥ Are you talking to a neighbor?

♥ Are you busy in the kitchen?

♥ Are you involved with the children?

♥ Are you taking care of work-related business?

How do you think he feels?

_____

_____

_____

_____

_____

What is his reaction?

_____

_____

_____

_____

_____

The ten-second kiss

Whenever you haven't seen each other for an extended period of time, make it a practice to give each other a kiss that lasts for at least ten seconds.

Love is a decision

Definition of love

"Love is that which causes one person to desire the most good to come to another and is willing to do whatever is necessary to bring it about."

—*Rev. C. W. Blout*—

Definition of romance

Romance is sending out a message to your mate about how special and desirable he is. It is recognizing his sexuality both in and *out* of the bedroom. It is the affirmation of your femininity and his masculinity. It's stopping in the mad rush of life to focus in on your partner as unique in your life.

Romance says,"You are number one on my list of priorities. You matter to me more than anyone else."

- ♥ More than my friends

- ♥ More than my relatives

- ♥ More than the children

- ♥ More than my coworkers

Men and women are different

Men and women have very different sexual needs and responses. When you understand these differences, you don't take it personally when your mate feels differently about something than you do.

We have to learn to appreciate our differences rather than attack each other for not feeling the same way.

See article by Jim Sanderson, Session 2, pages 41 and 42.

♥　A man's sexuality is an important aspect of his self - image. If he doesn't feel he is desirable, his self-esteem suffers.

♥　For most men, sex is the most meaningful demonstration of love and self-worth. He can't separate sex from love.

♥　A man has 17 glands which must be emptied regularly. If they aren't, it can lead to pain and illness.

♥　A woman can literally go through life and never have an orgasm without becoming physically ill. For a woman, hugging, kissing, and cuddling are important aspects of her fulfillment. Without foreplay or fore-thought, a woman can't feel complete.

♥　A man needs *sexual fulfillment* in order to respond emotionally.

♥　A woman needs *emotional fulfillment* in order to respond sexually.

Understanding our sexual differences

MEN

Sexual response ⫸
Intellectual processing = Emotional response

WOMEN

Emotional response ⫸
Intellectual processing = Sexual response

Liberated Male

Marital Love Needs Sexual Expression

By JIM SANDERSON

Nobody who writes for daily newspaper consumption is under the illusion that he is producing deathless prose, and so it always surprises me when one of my columns seems to take on a life of its own.

Often it's a request for a copy of something I'd forgotten I said years ago about raising kids, expressing love or taking charge of your life. I don't have a Xerox machine, alas, but the real estate office down the block kindly lets me use theirs.

Let me try to recapitulate one of the most frequent requests: it has to do with sex in longtime marriage. Dear Abby ran a letter from a woman who signed herself TIRED, which said:

"At age 50, after 30 years of marriage, I would like to forget about sex altogether. Believe me, I've paid my dues. I suspect that many (if not most) women get very little physical satisfaction out of sex; they just go through the motions because they want to do something for the men they love."

Abby polled her readers. Of the quarter of a million women who responded, more than 50% agreed with TIRED. I've seldom heard a statistic that depressed me more. Can you imagine spending your life with a woman who is only "going through the motions"?

Nobody ever comes right out and says that a woman like this has seriously diminished her husband as a man. Nobody ever tells her that she has mocked the word marriage. And that she is very lucky, indeed, to still have a husband to complain about.

It's women who insist endlessly that they can't have sex without love. But how can a married woman have love without sex, if it is physically possible? Doesn't she see that sex is the final stage you move to when words and gestures do not suffice to express the depths of your feeling?

Sex in marriage is love, the mystical union of not only two bodies but two souls. Marital love is debased when it becomes no better than simple affection, shared experience and kind words.

The most common complaint wives have is that husbands don't say the magical words *I love you* often enough. Sadly, because of their conditioning, it's very hard for some males to verbalize. But that doesn't mean they don't feel.

Often the sexual act is the best they can manage to express a whole range of emotions they have for the women who share their lives.

73a

Liberated Male

Two Sides of Sexuality in a Marriage

By JIM SANDERSON

My darling husband: I was so touched last night when you asked how you could make sex better for me, but I don't think I gave you a very good answer.

For me, as for most women, sex and love are so intertwined that I find it hard to think about them separately. I am always most responsive, and most thrilled, when I am feeling most in love with you. I am more likely to have difficulty reaching climax when I sense, even subconsciously, that some coldness or distance has crept into our relationship, or we have had an argument that hasn't been resolved.

Our love-making is always rewarding to me even if I haven't quite "made it" that night, if you will hold me in your arms afterward and hug and kiss and talk. I love the physical part, but it is the added emotional feeling that you give me then that leaves me with a glow all the next day. This is the reassurance that the spiritual part of our union is intact, and that my being your wife has a broad spectrum of meaning for you.

Casual Touching Appreciated

At the end of the day when you put your arms around me in the kitchen and kiss the back of my neck and hug me, I almost melt inside, even though there is nothing very sexual about it. I'd really like more of this casual touching any time of the day or night, a back rub or even a slight caress of the fingers just in passing. It keeps me in touch with you — keeps me wanting you.

You may find it a bit odd, but the word *respect* is a factor in my physical desire. The respect I have for you as a man and as a father, and the respect you give me in our daily life by listening to my opinions and in sharing your feelings.

So many men don't seem to do that, and all the exotic sexual technique in the world couldn't compensate, at least for me.

And he was moved to reply:

Dear wife: Thank you for taking the time to write such an eloquent explanation of your feelings. In a good marriage husbands do share much of this intertwining of love and sex, and I will try to respond even more in the areas you suggest.

But for males there is always an added element, and I need your help in this.

Many women think of sex in terms of responding to a man's advances. Maybe this is appropriate when we are young; the male libido then may be strong enough for two — to say the least. But we aren't kids anymore.

73b

All the research says a man's sex drive fades a little every year, but it's not really that. The pressures at work get tougher. Sometimes a man feels he's fighting for his life, and his sexual energy gets absorbed into the battle.

Drift Toward Sibling Relationship

There are family pressures, too, which you know about. I just want to say that a man's sexual power is not the same for all his life. If he wants to be faithful to his wife, he cuts off outside sources of erotic simulation. Some couples drift down to a gentle affection and kindness that is almost brotherly and sisterly.

I don't think you want that to happen to us any more that I do. I'm sure you rejoice when some kind of sacred spark of excitement jumps between us. I need your help to make it happen more often with greater intensity.   Hugs are fine. affection is lovely, but I need to know when there are sexual feelings stirring within you, too.

I want you to play a more important role in deciding when and where we will make love, and how. Your excitement provokes mine. Those "casual" caresses you speak of are pleasurable to me but sometimes I would like to think there are wild thoughts racing through your head- that you are planning some new and interesting menu not just for dinner that night, but for later. Surprise me, will you?

Dear partner: I know your body as well as my own, yet I feel there is always new territory to be explored, if we see our love as constant process of discovery and growth.

♥ A man gives love for sex.

♥ *A woman gives sex for love.*

♥ A man uses sex to say he's sorry, or to make up after an argument.

♥ *A woman wants to make up first and then have sex.*

♥ A man is stimulated by sight.

♥ *A woman is stimulated by words.*

♥ A man generally prefers sex in the morning, when his hormone level is at it's highest.

♥ *A woman generally prefers sex at night, when her hormone level is at it's highest.*

♥ A man can get excited immediately (much like a pile of dry leaves will burst into flames when ignited by a match).

♥ *A woman takes more time to become excited (like slow-burning charcoal. Just remember, once the charcoal gets going, it burns as hot as the leaves, and often stays hotter longer!)*

♥ For a man, sex provides the relaxation he needs for sleep.

♥ *Sex is the last thing a woman wants when she's tired.*

♥ After sex, men release a hormone that makes them sleepy.

♥ *After sex, women release a hormone that makes them wakeful. They want to cuddle, relate, and experience afterplay — not go to sleep.*

***Romance = Sensitivity +
Spontaneity + Creativity***

Increase your spontaneity

Up to now, we've been addressing sensitivity — being in tune to his needs.

♥   Making him feel special

♥   Understanding his world of stress and strain

♥   Appreciating his uniqueness

Now let's look at spontaneity.

***Idea + Decision + Action
= Spontaneity***

Spontaneity is the speed with which our decision to act or not act follows our thought. The faster we can go from the initial idea to the ultimate action determines our level of spontaneity.

You can become more spontaneous by being open to your ideas, deciding quickly how and when to implement the idea, and then following through.

With practice, you will find that:

♥   Great ideas will pop into your head more frequently

♥   Your ability to make quick decisions will increase

♥   You will do more things than you have ever done before.

EXAMPLES:

Scenario 1

You're in a mall shopping for a new sweater for yourself. You pass by the men's department on your way to sweaters.

Idea:

> *Gee, I'd really like to buy my mate a little "no occasion" gift, just because I love him.*

Decision:

> *I'll take a half-hour to look for something, so he knows I was thinking of him today.*

Action:

> *Buy him a new tie, have it gift-wrapped, and give it to him with a special card.*

Scenario 2

While you are shopping for an appliance you pass by the lingerie department.

Idea:

> *It's been so long since I had a sexy nightgown.*

Decision:

> *I'll buy one and surprise him tonight by wearing it, instead of my usual sweats.*

Action:

> *Buy a negligee and plan the surprise unveiling.*

Scenario 3

You're at work. You're really exhausted because you've been putting in extra hours and effort the last few weeks.

Idea:

I know I've really been neglecting my mate. What we need is a little time away—just the two of us.

Decision:

I'll just call a few nearby hotels and see what kind of weekend packages they offer.

Action:

Book the room and send your mate a sexy invitation, asking him to meet you at the hotel on the designated evening.

Before you know it, your mate will say, "Boy, are you becoming a spontaneous person. I never know what to expect. You are the most exciting woman alive."

Boredom

1. Repetition and predictability are the center of boredom.

2. The best way not to have a boring relationship is not to be a boring person.

3. One of the best ways to alleviate boredom is to plan a surprise for the one you love.

A surprise is a wonderful way to show your mate that you care and to create a lifelong memory.

Look at the following list and pick out the one that is *not you.* Remember, when you do something completely out of character your heart will beat faster and your adrenalin will flow.

*Do something unpre-
dictable, spontaneous,
and different.*

21 ways to create a memory

1. Call him at work and pretend you are a secret admirer
    (it will only take him a second to play along with you).
    Tell him you can't stand it any longer—you just have to
    meet him. Pick a bar, if you really want to be daring, or
    a hotel or restaurant and make a date to meet him
    there. Show up wearing a blond wig if you have dark
    hair, or a dark wig if you have blond hair. Wear lots of
    jewelry if you are conservative, a business suit if you
    are usually casual. Just pretend you are someone else
    who is madly and passionately in love with this man.

2. Go on a date and leave your underwear in your drawer
    at home. When you get in the car, a sneak preview is in
    order.

3. Check into a nice hotel in town and have a romantic
    evening together.

4. Have a boudoir photo session done of yourself and
    present the album to him.

5. Light the bathroom with candles and draw a bubble
    bath . After you get into the tub, ask him to bring you a
    towel and watch how fast he joins you.

6. Wear a sexy negligee under your regular clothing. Do a
    strip tease, removing the top layers piece by piece. Give
    him some sexy underwear or robe to wear.

7. Before he wakes up in the morning, write on the mirror
    in red lipstick :

    *"Roses and red
    Violets are blue
    I feel quite sexy
    Please come home at two."*

    Or:

    *"You Tarzan,
    Me Jane.
    Let's swing tonight."*

8.   Write him love notes and stick them in places he's sure to find them.

♥   On the mirror while he's shaving:

"You are now looking at the most handsome face on earth."

♥   On the toilet seat:

"Please take good care of my favorite part of your terrific body."

♥   On the kitchen counter or refrigerator door:

"Good morning, sweetheart. Have a wonderful breakfast so that the world's greatest lover will be full of energy."

♥   On the steering wheel of his car:

"Drive safely. You are the most important person in my life!"

♥   In his briefcase:

"Have a great day at work. I can't wait to see you tonight, when I can hold you in my arms again."

9.   Telephone him at work or leave a message on his voice mail. Let him know he's the sexiest man alive and you can't wait to see that big hunk tonight.

10. Cover the bed with rose petals. Tell him he's made your life a bed of roses and you want to celebrate by making love to him *in* a bed of roses.

11. Before he leaves work, call and tell him you are waiting for him with bells on. When he comes home, be wearing bells on your wrists and ankles—and nothing else.

12. Fill his car with balloons. Put a note in each balloon telling him why he's so special. Tape a long needle to the windshield with a note explaining that the only way he can get into his car is to pop the balloons and read the notes.

13. When he's away on a business trip, send him a package containing your most sexy nightgown sprayed with your favorite perfume and an enticing note. Let him anticipate his homecoming.

14. Buy shampoo, body lotion, clear nail polish and a nail file. Give him a clue everyday for a week, leading up to an evening of relaxation just for him. When the special night arrives, shampoo his hair and massage his scalp. Give him a manicure and pedicure, including clear nail polish. Finish with a full-body massage, using the body lotion. Save the best part of the massage for last.

15. Plan a romantic picnic. Pack a basket with your favorite food and wine and find a secluded spot. Take along a tablecloth and blanket. Bring a book of love poems and take turns reading them to each other.

16. Plan a day at the zoo, carnival, or amusement park. Cotton candy, hot dogs, popcorn, and drippy ice cream cones keep your love young.

17. Surprise him with satin sheets on the bed. Add to the sensual experience with silk pajamas for him and a silk nightgown for you.

18. He'll think he's died and gone to heaven the night he comes home to find a welcoming note taped to the door, the house dark except for a candlelit dining table set with a beautifully prepared dinner, and you waiting for him in a sexy negligee.

19. Prepare a meal and serve it with no utensils. Feed each other using only your hands. Spice up the meal with kisses between each course.

20. Send your mate a note explaining that you're sending him on a love hunt. Tell him to follow the instructions precisely and he will be rewarded. Send him from place to place to pick up a purchase that has been made in advance and that is waiting for him with additional instructions. For example, send him to the liquor store where a bottle good champagne is waiting with his name on it and a note telling him the next stop is the florist. At the florist he will find a bouquet of flowers and another note. Next stop could be a party supply

store where a dozen balloons that say "I love you" are waiting. Then a music store for his favorite tape, and last his favorite restaurant, where he finds you waiting for him. After dinner, excuse yourself and tell him you're going to the ladies' room. As you leave, ask the waiter to deliver a note to your husband telling him to meet you at a particular hotel in 30 minutes. This is when he gets his reward.

22. Prepare a tribute album to him. Fill it with pictures of him and cut appropriate captions for the photos from magazines.

Use your imagination!

There are hundreds of little things you can do to let him know you love him and that you feel lucky to be sharing your life with him.

Don't postpone romance until:

♥   The children are older

♥   You have more time

♥   You have more money

People who postpone romance find that:

♥   The days turn into weeks

♥   The weeks turn into months

♥   The months turn into years

Use it or lose it!

Until finally, you are two people who are living as room-mates—or worse—as complete strangers.

If you don't *use* your romantic imagination, it will become more difficult as time goes on to put your wonderful ability into action. The more you act, the more ideas will come to you.

Discover the excitement of being the one who ignites the flame of romance!

HOMEWORK ASSIGNMENT

1. Make one night this week really special. Take the time to think about what would turn him on. Your goal is to plan a surprise that will create a memory. He'll feel special and important— and thrilled at all this attention just for him.

2. Buy yourself a special negligee. Be daring and wild. If you are inclined to say, "That's not me," then don't be you. Be someone else. Be a woman who is romantic and sexy.

Session 5: Support Your Local Self

"This above all: To thine own self be true,
And it must follow, as night the day,
Thou canst not then be false to any man.

—William Shakespeare—

The time of greatest unhappiness with your mate is usually the time you are the most unhappy with yourself.

Do you consider yourself to be:

☐ Very happy

☐ Often happy

☐ Frequently unhappy

☐ Unhappy most of the time

When you are unhappy, do you feel that any of the following are reasons for your unhappiness:

☐ The way people treat you

☐ Lack of money

☐ Lack of time

☐ Lack of freedom

☐ Physical appearance

☐ Mental ability

☐ Unfulfilled dreams

☐ Too much responsibility

Are you a member of the "If Only" club?

Blaming people or circumstances outside ourselves is a way of avoiding the truth.

> **If only** ... I were ten pounds lighter, I would be happy.
>
> **If only** ... I had more money, I would be happy.
>
> **If only** ... I had a baby, I would be happy.
>
> **If only** ... I had a nicer house, I would be happy.
>
> **If only** ... I were prettier, I would be happy.

Use this space to fill in your own dreams (talent, intelligence, ability, etc.)

If only ...

_____

_____

_____

_____

_____

... I would be happy.

If you are a member of the "If Only" club you are robbing yourself of the only thing you can really be sure of — the **present!**

Be here now!

Whenever you find yourself drifting off to the past or dreaming about the future, call yourself back to the present by saying out loud:

> "Hey, (use your name), **be here now!**

*Yesterday is a can-
celled check, tomorrow
is a promissory note.
Today is cash in the
bank.*

Examples:

Scenario 1:

> You are at the beauty salon, having your hair done. As you lie with your head in the shampoo bowl, you begin to worry about all the things you need to do when you leave.
>
> Call yourself back to the present — "Hey, Barbara, **Be here now!**" —and just concentrate on how wonderful it feels to have your head massaged.

Scenario 2:

> You have just completed your third day of a new diet. You start to feel discouraged as you recall how often you have failed to stick to a diet in the past.
>
> Call yourself back to the present — "Hey, Joyce. **Be here now!**"— and concentrate on how terrific you are for declining the dessert you really wanted last night. Congratulate yourself for your willpower, **now!**

*Don't postpone happi-
ness for some future
event.*

Don't postpone:

> Buying ...
> Doing ...
> Experiencing ...

... until you have the time, the money, or the perfect opportunity. That time may never come!

"Life is what's happening while you're making other plans."

—John Lennon—

Our thoughts create our mood

Happiness is a state of mind. Our thoughts create our mood.

      Negative thoughts = Bad mood
      Positive thoughts   = Good mood

Depression is usually preceded by a series of negative thoughts.

Depression is caused by the belief that:

1.   We aren't in control of our lives. That we are victims in life, rather than the creator of our lives.

2.   That change should be directed toward others, rather than ourselves.

Remember—You are only a victim once, The second time, you are a volunteer.

You don't have the power to change other people. You only have the power to change yourself.

Don't worry — be happy

Worry is a waste of time. It is nothing more than an image of the future that you don't want to happen.

Even if your worst fear should become a reality, why go through the experience twice — once in your mind and once in reality?

List some of your worries here.

_____
_____
_____
_____
_____
_____
_____
_____
_____
_____
_____

Become a warrior, not a worrier.

The mind can't hold a negative thought and a positive thought about the same thing at the same time. When a negative thought pops into your head, fight back and change the picture to something positive.

Don't create negative energy. Create positive energy by creating a positive picture of the future.

Example:

1. Your husband is an hour late arriving home from work and you haven't heard from him. You picture him in an accident or having a rendezvous with another woman.

   Replace that picture with one of him returning home safely and having a good explanation.

2. You're due for a promotion. You picture a colleague in your office getting the promotion instead of you.

   Fight back by changing the picture. Imagine yourself jumping for joy because you were just told that it's you they decided to promote.

Feel the fear and do it anyway!

Action is the single most effective way to overcome depression, anxiety, stress, fear, worry, or guilt.

Some of us are kept from action because of fear. There is nothing wrong with fear. Just feel the fear and do it anyway.

Here are two sentences that you must never say again.

1.   There is really nothing I can do about it.

2.   That's just the way things are.

Every time one of those thoughts pops into your mind, resist that helpless belief. Replace it with something like this:

1.   I'm not sure what to do in this situation, but I'll think of something. I just need some time.

2.   While things may be bad at this time, I have the power to change them.

Write down an experience that upset you this week.

_____

_____

_____

_____

_____

What two things can you do to change the situation?

_____

_____

_____

_____

_____

_____

How can you view the situation differently, so that it becomes a positive learning experience?

_____
_____
_____
_____
_____
_____

"God grant me the serenity to accept the things I cannot change,
the courage to change the things I can,
and the wisdom to know the difference."

—Serenity Prayer—

The only way to get rid of a hurt is to confront the person who hurt you.

Unfinished business

No matter how many people you complain to about the person who hurt you, the hurt will not go away until you tell the person to their face what they did and how you feel.

- ♥ Most effective way — face to face

- ♥ Next most effective way — on the telephone

- ♥ Another effective way — in a letter

- ♥ Least effective way — by telling someone else and hoping they relay the message

Don't expect to change the other person. The reason you are confronting them is to get rid of unnecessary baggage — to free yourself of anger. As soon as you do it, you'll feel ten pounds lighter.

If you get a positive result, great. But, this is not about who's right or wrong. It's about finishing unfinished business!

Lists, lists, lists

The stewing is worse than the doing.

It takes three times the energy to worry about what needs to be done than to actually do it.

It takes:

♥   Three times the energy to worry about a phone call you don't want to make than to actually make the call

♥   Three times the energy to worry about cleaning the house, than to do it

♥   Three times the energy to worry about going on a date, than to actually go

Worry is draining.
Action is exhilarating.

Write down five things you have to do tomorrow. As you complete them, cross out each one with a bright yellow marker. Start with the one you want to do least, and get it out of the way first.

1. _____
2. _____
3. _____
4. _____
5. _____

Procrastination takes too much energy. If you put off doing the things you don't want to do, you won't have the energy left to do the things you want to do.

Love is like knowledge: The more you have, the more you can share.

What are some of the things you'd like to do — just for yourself? Be selfish!

Time for just you

The more you do for yourself, the more of you there'll be to give to others.

_____
_____
_____
_____
_____
_____
_____
_____
_____
_____

Self-Discovery

Two questions for self-discovery

♥   If I weren't getting paid for what I'm doing, would I continue?

♥   If I had only one year to live, would I continue doing what I'm doing?

Let your inner guide answer these questions.

Just be you

The hardest thing in the world to be is what someone else wants you to be.

The easiest thing in the world to be is **you.**

"Just for today I will live through the next 12 hours and not tackle my whole life problem at once.

Just for today I will improve my mind. I will learn something useful. I will read something that requires effort, thought and concentration.

Just for today I will be agreeable. I will look my best, speak in a well-modulated voice, be courteous and considerate.

Just for today I will not find fault with anyone. I will not try to change or improve anyone but myself.

Just for today I will have a program. I might not follow it exactly, but I will have it. It will save me from two enemies— hurry and indecision.

Just for today I will exercise my character in two ways. I will do a good turn and keep it a secret. If anyone finds out, it won't count.

Just for today I will do two things I don't want to do, just for exercise.*

Just for today I will be unafraid. Especially will I be unafraid to enjoy what is beautiful, to love and to believe that those I love, love me. I will remember that as I give my best to the world, the world will give back to me."

—Author unknown—

*(See homework assignment.)

HOMEWORK ASSIGNMENT

1. Be aware of your mental processes. Call yourself back to the present as often as you can this week.

2. Complete some unfinished business. Feel the fear and do it anyway.

3. Do two things this week that you have been avoiding.

4. Get organized. Write a list each night of the things you need to do the next day and cross off each task as you complete it.

5. Let your inner guide lead you — not other people's expectations.

Session 6: Feelings Just Are

"Not to be aware of one's feelings, not to understand them
or know how to use or express them
is worse than being blind, deaf or paralyzed.
Not to feel is not to be alive.
More than anything else feelings make us human.
Feelings make us all kindred."

— David Viscott, M. D. —

Feelings cause all of us to experience:

♥ Pleasure

♥ Pain

EXAMPLE:

Imagine two 25-year-old women, financially equal, being told they're pregnant.

♥ One might feel *happy* because she's going to have a baby.

♥ One might feel *anxiety* because she's not ready for motherhood.

Or, imagine six women arriving late for a meeting that has begun without them.

♥ One feels *angry* because the meeting started without her.

♥ One *worries* that she has missed something important.

♥ One is *afraid* that the boss will disapprove of her for coming late.

♥ One is *frustrated* because she has to interrupt the meeting.

♥ One feels *happy* that she finally arrived.

♥ One feels *self-conscious* because she knows everyone is going to look at her as she walks in.

Or, think about two women getting fired from a job.

♥ One feels *relieved* because she hated her job but didn't have enough confidence to leave on her own.

♥ One feels *depressed* because she doesn't want to look for another job.

Who is right?

Feelings are not right or wrong—they just are.

In all the above situations, no one is right or wrong. Feelings are not right or wrong—they just are; and they need to be recognized. Each person will respond differently to the same situation — given his or her particular set of circumstances and total life experiences up to that moment.

How we lose touch with our feelings:

From the time we were children, many of us have been taught to deny our feelings. For example, we may have been told:

- ♥ Don't cry (when we had a sad experience).

- ♥ It doesn't hurt (when we scraped our knee or got a shot from the doctor).

- ♥ Apologize to your brother (when we're not sorry).

- ♥ Eat all of your supper (when we're really not hungry).

Adults often teach us to lie.

As young children, we all start out in life congruent with our feelings, and capable of sharing them truthfully with the significant adults in our lives (parents; grandparents; teachers). For example:

♥ "Did you break this vase?" This question initially will get a nod or a yes — the child has been totally honest. Unfortunately, many adults will respond to the child's honesty by shouting:

"You've been very bad! Go to your room! Just wait until your daddy gets home!"

This typical scenario teaches a child that by telling the truth, punishment could follow.

Even in the classroom, children can be taught to lie.

Do you recognize this one?

"Okay, class, who was laughing when I was writing on the blackboard?"

Unfortunately, the child who says "I was" often ends up in trouble or in the principal's office.

A teacher who is interested in teaching children to tell the truth would have said:

"Mary, thank you for telling the truth. Now please, don't disturb the class — this is an important lesson everyone should be listening to."

The point is:

As adults, we continue to lie because as children we learned that telling the truth often results in punishment.

Beginning early in life, we gradually perfected the art of covering up and ignoring our own real feelings.

WE ....*Denied*
Pretended
Lied

After all, we wanted to be loved and accepted by our parents.

Dis/ease

When we're not releasing our own feelings, we are not at ease. Experts like Dr. Bernie Seigel have found that cancer patients are often compulsive people-pleasers. They sacrifice themselves for the good of others.

Often — feelings that are covered up manifest themselves in DISEASE.

_____

_____

_____

_____

_____

_____

_____

_____

_____

_____

Write down an experience you've had where you covered up your own feelings in order to protect someone else's.

How did that make you feel?

_____

_____

_____

_____

_____

_____

_____

_____

_____

Understanding your feelings better

When you're not certain how or what you're feeling, the following list might help.

REMEMBER — try to decide HOW you feel, as well as WHY you feel that way.

HATE

1. Bitter
2. Resentful
3. Spiteful
4. Horrified
5. Loathing

FEAR

1. Anxious
2. Suspicious
3. Apprehensive
4. Terrified
5. Worried

ANGER

1. Mad
2. Hostile
3. Displeased
4. Offended
5. Resentful

HAPPINESS

1. Enthusiastic
2. Joyful
3. Delighted
4. Pleased
5. Contented

LOVE

1. Affectionate
2. Tender
3. Devoted
4. Fond
5. Passionate

CONFUSION

1. Mixed up
2. Disorganized
3. Bewildered
4. Uncertain
5. Perplexed

SADNESS

1. Grief stricken
2. Dejected
3. Sorrowful
4. Unhappy
5. Gloomy

DISAPPOINTMENT

1. Unhappy
2. Dissatisfied
3. Defeated
4. Hurt
5. Unfulfilled

Millie's Mother's Red Dress

It hung there in the closet
While she was dying, Mother's red dress,
Like a gash in the row
Of dark, old clothes
She had worn away her life in.

They had called me home,
And I knew when I saw her
She wasn't going to last.

When I saw the dress, I said,
"Why, Mother — how beautiful!
I've never seen it on you."

I've never worn it," she slowly said.
'Sit down, Millie — I'd like to undo
A lesson or two before I go, if I can."

I sat by her bed,
And she sighed a bigger breath
Than I thought she could hold.
"Now that I'll soon be gone,
I can see some things.
Oh, I taught you good —
But I taught you wrong."

"What do you mean, Mother?"

"Well — I always thought
That a good woman never takes her turn,
That she's just for doing for somebody else.
Do here, do there, always keep
Everybody else's wants tended and make sure
Yours are at the bottom of the heap.

Maybe someday you'll get to them,
But of course you never do.
My life was like that— doing for your dad,
Doing for the boys, for your sisters, for you."

"You did — everything a mother could."

— MORE —

"Oh, Millie, Millie, it was no good —
For you — for him. Don't you see?
I did you the worst of wrongs
I asked nothing — for me!

"Your father in the other room,
All stirred up and staring at the walls —
When the doctor told him, he took
It bad — came to my bed and all but shook
The life right out of me. 'You can't die,
Do you hear? What'll become of me?
What'll become of me?'
It'll be hard, all right, when I go.
He can't even find the frying pan, you know.

"And you children.
I was a free ride for everybody, everywhere.
I was the first one up and the last one down
Seven days out of the week.
I always took the toast that got burned.
And the very smallest piece of pie.
I look at how some of your brothers treat their
wives now,
And it makes me sick, 'cause it was me
That taught it to them. And they learned.
They learned that a woman doesn't
Even exist except to give.
Why, every single penny that I could save
Went for your clothes, or your books,
Even when it wasn't necessary.
Can't even remember once when I took
Myself downtown to buy something beautiful —
For me.

"Except last year when I got that red dress.
I found I had twenty dollars
That wasn't especially spoke for.
I was on my way to pay it extra on the washer.
But somehow — I came home with this big box.
Your father really gave it to me then.
'Where you going to wear a thing like that to —
Some opera or something?'
And he was right, I guess.
I've never, except in the store,
Put on that dress.

— MORE —

"Oh, Millie — I always thought if you take
Nothing for yourself in this world,
You'd have it all in the next somehow.
I don't believe that anymore
I think the Lord wants us to have something-
Here — and now.

"And I'm telling you, Millie, if some miracle
Could get me off this bed, you could look
For a different mother, 'cause I would be one.
Oh, I passed up my turn so long
I would hardly know how to take it.
But I'd learn, Millie.
I would learn!"

It hung there in the closet
While she was dying. Mother's red dress,
Like a gash in the row
Of dark, old clothes
She had worn away her life in.

Her last words to me were these:
"Do me the honor, Millie,
Of not following in my footsteps.
Promise me that."

I promised.
She caught her breath.
Then Mother took her turn
In death.

Guilt

Guilt is nothing more than you not feeling like someone else said you should.

List some things you wanted to have or do, but couldn't because of GUILT.

_____
_____
_____
_____
_____
_____
_____

Now describe your behavior as a result of denying yourself.

_____
_____
_____
_____
_____
_____
_____

Describe what you think your behavior would be if you permitted yourself to do or have what you really want.

_____
_____
_____
_____
_____
_____

FEEL THE GUILT AND DO IT ANYWAY!

It's very difficult to get rid of guilt feelings — and in most cases, next to impossible. So, if you want happiness, why bother? Just feel the guilt and do it anyway.

Feelings just are

To handle your feelings effectively, you must learn to:

(1)   Recognize them as your own

(2)   Share them with the people you care about

Remember, only you could possibly know for certain what you feel — others may be able to guess — but only you know for sure.

Poor communication often begins with not knowing what you are really feeling.

Couples who consistently deal with and share their true feelings will foster a greater relationship than couples who keep their feelings to themselves.

A typical "real life" scenario:

In an attempt to understand how strong feelings can lead to poor communications and conflict, please envision the following scenario involving you and your mate at his company's annual Christmas party:

♥ *Setting*
Your mate is spending a great deal of time talking and laughing with his attractive, 23-year-old secretary.

♥ *Assumption*
He would rather be with her than with you.

♥ *Feeling response*
Although you will most likely be unaware of what you are actually feeling, *anger* will be quite dominant.

♥ *Your verbal response*
"Jim, you sure acted like a fool tonight."

♥ *End result*
An irritated mate and, perhaps, even an argument.

But remember—feelings just are; they are neither good nor bad.

If you had been more aware of your true feelings, this same scenario might have ended like this:

♥ *Your verbal response*
"Jim, when I saw you spending so much time laughing and talking to your pretty secretary tonight, I felt rejected, hurt and angry. It made me feel you'd rather be with her more than with me."

♥ *End result*
Since you have not blamed him in any way, there is no reason for him to be irritated and/or argumentative. This greatly improves the likelihood that he will comfort you.

Remember, with feelings:

♥ Coming to grips with your real feelings is important.

♥ You are unique — one of a kind.

♥ Being true to yourself will *not* prevent others from satisfying their own needs.

Negative feelings:

In order to foster and maintain a sound, fulfilling relationship, we must express our *negative*, as well as our *positive* feelings. Whenever we have been treated poorly, ignored, insulted, ridiculed, or teased, we have a right to express our anger, hurt and disappointment.

Anger:

Anger is hurt that is covered up. The longer you keep from verbalizing your hurt feelings, the more angry you'll become. Confessing that you are capable of being hurt is an act of *strength* rather than a *weakness*. By admitting you are angry, you are really saying, "You hurt me, and what I want is for you to love and care about me."

The problem:

Most couples argue about *opinions* instead of *feelings*. Unfortunately, it's not that easy.

Using the "I" statement

"I" statements take responsibility; "You" statements place blame.

By using "I" statements, we can learn to deal with the problem — and refrain from threatening our mate.

Effective Communication	Ineffective Communication
"I really get lonely when I don't hear from you all day."	"How come you never call me like other husbands do?"
"I really want a hug when you come home because I missed you."	"Why don't you ever hug me anymore?"
"I would really love to spend an hour with you when you get home."	"You are always so tired when you get home."
"When you don't call me to let me know you'll be late for dinner, I feel unimportant to you."	"It's obvious you care more about your job than me, since you're late for dinner."

Describe a problem with your mate that causes you to get angry.

_____

_____

_____

_____

_____

Now rewrite the problem, using an "I" statement.

_____

_____

_____

_____

_____

The scale of 1 – 10

In order to get more in touch with your own feelings, as well as your mate's, try this extremely useful method.

Whenever you are about to agree to something, ask yourself:

"On a scale of 1 – 10, how much do I really want to do this?"

If the answer falls anywhere between zero and three — *don't do it!*

EXAMPLES:

1. A friend asks if you could watch her children on the weekend. You've already made plans. Ask yourself:

   "On a scale of 1 – 10, how much do I want to do this?"

   If the answer is one, you simply say:

   "I'm sorry, but I've made other plans. Next time, with a little more notice, I'd be glad to help you out."

2. A coworker asks you to go out and have a drink after work. You really want to go home. Take a moment to mentally do the scale and, if there is no desire on your part, instead of going so as to not hurt her feelings and ignore your feelings, politely decline the invitation.

3. The school PTA president calls you up and asks if you would like to contribute to the annual cake sale. On the scale of 1 – 10, you find it to be a 7. *Go for it!*

Using the scale as a couple:

Often couples think they are doing each other a favor when, in fact, neither one really wants to participate. This results in both partners being angry, because neither one recognizes the sacrifice the other has made.

If an activity involves your mate, ask him to use the same scale. You are invited as a couple to someone's house for a party. You are about a 4 on the scale, your mate is a 2. *Don't go.* If your mate is a 9 and you are a 4, then go. At least your mate will be pleased.

Other ways to use the 1 – 10 scale.

This method is also useful in finding out:

♥ How much pain a person is experiencing. If it's an 8 – 10, it's time to see a doctor.

♥ How much your son or daughter loves his girlfriend or boyfriend. (You'll know whether to panic or not!)

♥ How happy or disappointed you or your mate is about a given situation.

Being playful

Inside every man, no matter how successful, powerful and strong, there is a little boy waiting to come out and *play*. The woman that can provide the playground becomes indispensable in his life.

An intimate way of relating and communicating is by using:

- ♥ Pet names
- ♥ Baby talk

Lover Buns	Love Bucket
Pussy Cat	Stud Muffin
Snookums	Sunshine
Lovey Dovey	Lambie Pie
Pumpkin	Lover Boy
Sugar Pot	Pudding Pie
Baby Duck	Hunkey Poo
Hon Bun	Bubba Bear
Poopsie	Big Kahuna
Sweet Cake	Honey Buns
Sweet Pea	Apple Dumpling
Sweet Cheeks	Peaches
Tiger Lover	Teddy Bear
Stud Dumpling	

Baby talk and pet names can work great — especially when your mate is:

- ♥ Too serious

- ♥ Doesn't want to do something you want to

- ♥ Ignoring you

- ♥ Unaware of something you want very badly

Exaggeration:

Absurd exaggeration, for purposes of emphasis, can often allow your mate to see how he made you angry more quickly than confrontation can. The following examples will often even produce laughter and make him feel even more masculine:

♥ "You beast — I'm never going to talk to you again!"

♥ "That does it. I'll never wash your shorts again!"

♥ "If you don't quit teasing me right now, I'll never scratch your back again."

♥ "I'm never going to cook again — and that's the good news!"

♥ Somebody, somewhere must love me!

Remember, men love this type of behavior. In the final analysis, you'll be able to express your anger (over minor and medium affronts) and eliminate many potential resentments and grudges from forming.

Make a wish list

Women are usually more intuitive than men, and because they possess this quality, they assume that their mate does too.

Most men do not have ESP. They cannot read your mind.

Ask and you shall receive.

A fantastic method for creating a great relationship and getting your needs satisfied is for each of you to develop a separate wish list. The ground rules are that you can jot down anything your mate could give you that would bring you great happiness.

Some examples from previous classes are:

♥ Take a walk together on the beach once a week.

♥ Have lunch with me at least once a month.

♥ Tell me how much you love me at least twice a day.

♥ Call me up during the day just to say you miss me.

♥ Kiss me hello and good-bye every day, for at least 10 seconds per kiss.

♥ Help me with my housework once in a while.

♥ Hug me, touch me and kiss me at times other than when we're making love.

SUMMARY

Although we have covered a great deal in Session 6, the following summarizes the key points best:

1. Always share your feelings with your mate — when they are fresh — without attacking. Use "I" statements.

2. Strive to trade your anger for guilt. Remember, feel the guilt and do it anyway.

3. Be certain your mate knows that you will never be upset or angry with him if he tells you the truth. He must be convinced it is safe to express his real feelings. Use the 1 – 10 scale.

4. In order for your mate to satisfy your needs, he must know what they are. Ask for what you want.

5. Strive to be playful. To accomplish this, use baby talk, childlike mannerisms and pet names.

6. You and your mate should independently create a "Wish List." To gain the most from this exercise, share and discuss your lists together.

The beginning

Although we've reached the end of the program, it's really just the beginning. Growing in a relationship takes effort, commitment and concentration on an ongoing, continuous basis.

Every few months, when you find yourself backsliding, take out your workbook and work through one chapter at a time. Review all the material once again.

Remember, whatever you did to get your mate, you need to do three times as much to keep him. Never take your relationship and his love for granted.

Fairy tales can come true. Your Prince Charming — your knight in shining armor — your hero — is waiting to be discovered.